TV Heat

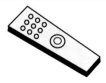

Written by Jonny Zucker

Illustrated by Sally Newton

Titles in Full Flight 4

Badger Publishing Limited
15 Wedgwood Gate, Pin Green Industrial Estate,
Stevenage, Hertfordshire SG1 4SU
Telephone: 01438 356907. Fax: 01438 747015
www.badger-publishing.co.uk
enquiries@badger-publishing.co.uk

TV Heat ISBN 1 84691 030 7
        ISBN 978-1-84691-030-2

Text © Jonny Zucker 2006
Complete work © Badger Publishing Limited 2006

Series Editor: Jonny Zucker
Publisher: David Jamieson
Commissioning Editor: Carrie Lewis
Editor: Paul Martin
Design: Fiona Grant
Illustration: Sally Newton
Printed and bound in China through Colorcraft Ltd., Hong Kong

TV Heat

Contents

TV Hell

Kate Alton slammed her bedroom door and flopped down onto her bed. Her mum, Debbie, was driving her mad.

Debbie was a famous TV star. She had her own show called *At home with the Altons.* On the show, a different group of famous people came to live in their house each week. Ten TV cameras were in the house all of the time to film Debbie and Kate and the people who were living with them.

Every night, Debbie did a 'Diary Spot' where she talked about the things that had gone on in the house that day. Millions of people watched *At home with the Altons.*

When the show first started, Kate loved it. She got to meet lots of famous people and became a bit of a TV star herself. But now, a year later, she was sick of having cameras in her house the whole time. She was tired of TV people coming into her bedroom without knocking. And she'd had enough of people seeing her in the street and asking, 'Aren't you that girl off the telly?'

Last week, four female soap stars had lived with Kate and her mum. Kate had hated them. They all talked too loudly, wore too much make up and looked at themselves in the mirror every ten seconds.

Kate pulled over a pillow and got comfy on her bed. Why couldn't she have a normal mum like everyone else?

Her best mate Jaz had a normal mum. Jaz's mum did the shopping and cooked. Kate's mum always got other people to do those things. Kate closed her eyes. She'd had enough of her mum's stupid TV show. She'd *really* had enough.

Nightmare!

Later that day, Kate was with Jaz in the local shopping mall.

"My mum and her show are driving me crazy," Kate said.

"Really?" asked Jaz. "It *is* pretty cool to have a TV show filmed in your house."

"It *used to be* cool, but it's not any more," said Kate. "I never get any peace. There are cameras and wires and TV people in the house all of the time."

"Have you told your mum you're fed up?" asked Jaz.

"No. She wouldn't understand. She lives for the show."

"So what are you going to do?" asked
Jaz.

"I don't know," replied Kate.

When Kate got home, her mum and the TV show producer, Sally Clark, were sitting on the wall at the front of the house and laughing.

Sally Clark wasn't too bad, but Kate wished she'd find another family for the show.

"What's funny?" asked Kate.

"We've just got some brilliant guests for the beginning of next month," said Sally.

"Who are they?" asked Kate.

"We've got four world famous rugby players coming to live with us for a week," grinned Debbie. "Isn't that great?"

Kate groaned.

Four rugby players? Great?

No way – it would be a nightmare!

Talk It Out

The next week, a group of famous magicians were 'At home with the Altons'.

The magicians kept on making things disappear. Kate's hairbrush and her favourite shoes went missing. They turned up later, but Kate was really angry.

Then a TV guy burst into her room when she was on the phone to Jaz.

"Go away!" Kate shouted.

"Great shot!" laughed the guy, pointing the camera in her face.

When he'd left her room, Kate moaned to Jaz. "If I have to spend one more second with these magicians, I'll go crazy!" she moaned.

"They'll be gone soon," replied Jaz.

"Great!" said Kate. "Then I have the rugby players to look forward to."

"Well, tell your mum how you feel," said Jaz.

That night, after her mum had finished filming that day's 'Diary Spot', Kate went to talk to her in the back garden.

"Mum," Kate began. "About the show…"

"It's fab isn't it?" beamed Debbie.

"I know you love it," Kate said, "but I've had enough of it."

Debbie frowned. "What do you mean?"

"You know, having people in the house all of the time, the cameras being all over the place…"

"Come on, Kate. Every girl your age would love it! You're famous! And you get to meet all of these famous people."

"But you don't understand, Mum. The famous people are all *your* guests. I don't choose them. I hate it."

"Well I hate *your* loud music, but I live with it," said her mum.

"That's not the same!" cried Kate.

At that second, Debbie's mobile went. "Hang on a second, Kate, I have to take this call," she said.

Kate left her mum to her phone call. An idea had just formed in her mind.

There was only one thing for it. She *had* to escape this TV hell.

She thought about it for the next hour and made up her mind. She'd give it a couple of weeks and then she'd run away.

Getting Out

Two weeks later, Kate was in her room listening to a CD.

The last two weeks had been awful. A group of circus people and a team of astronauts had each spent a week 'At home with the Altons'.

It was Friday night. The rugby players were coming on Monday. But Kate would be gone by then. Her running away plan was ready – she was going tomorrow night.

She'd go to Jaz's first. She hadn't told Jaz this, because Jaz might try and talk her out of it. But Jaz would be okay and Jaz's mum was really nice. Kate could probably stay there for a bit while she thought of what to do next.

Kate was checking her list of what she'd need, when she heard loud voices coming from the kitchen. It was her mum and Sally.

She went down to the kitchen to see what was going on.

Debbie and Sally both looked up when she came in.

"What's going on?" Kate asked.

"We just got some bad news," said Debbie. "The rugby players have let us down. They have some special match in New Zealand they have to play in."

"Well, just get some other guests," said Kate.

"It's Friday night," said Debbie. "The show starts on Monday. We may not be able to get any more guests in such short time."

"So, what will you do?" asked Kate.

"No guests, no show," Sally said with a long face.

"The TV people will be very cross with us," said Debbie.

"I need to make lots of phone calls," said Sally.

Kate could see her mum and Sally were both upset, but she had other things on her mind.

By tomorrow night she'd be out of here.

Saturday evening. Five pm.

Kate had finished packing her bag. She had everything she needed. She would be at Jaz's in fifteen minutes and then she could plan what to do next.

Downstairs she could hear Sally on the phone, trying to find some new guests. It didn't sound like Sally was having any luck.

Kate zipped up her bag and opened her bedroom door very slowly.

She stepped out but saw her mum just in front of her, going down the stairs.

Kate held back. When her mum was out of sight, she'd go downstairs and hurry out of the front door.

But as Kate looked on in horror, her mum tripped over a camera wire on the stairs and went crashing down the last few steps.

Debbie yelled in pain.

Kate put her bag down and ran downstairs.

Debbie was lying at the bottom of the steps, holding her right leg in pain.

"Mum, are you okay?" shouted Kate.

"I'm okay," replied Debbie, "but I think I've broken my leg."

Change Of Plan

Sally Clark took Debbie to the hospital. They came back two hours later. Debbie *had* broken her leg. It was in plaster.

"It's a disaster!" moaned Debbie, resting her leg on a chair in the kitchen and talking to Sally.

"Losing our guests is bad enough," said Debbie. "But the doctor said I have to rest my leg in bed for a week. There's no way I can present the show from my bed. People will laugh at me! How can we do the show with no guests and no presenter?"

Sally shrugged her shoulders. "I'll think of something," she said.

But it wasn't Sally who thought of something. It was Kate.

As Sally came out of the kitchen, Kate was waiting for her.

"I know what you can do for this week's show," Kate said.

"Really?" asked Sally.

They went to the living room and Kate told Sally her idea.

Sally began to smile.

"You know what, Kate," grinned Sally. "That's a great idea! Let's do it!"

On Monday night at 8 o'clock, millions of people sat down in front of their TVs for 'At home with the Altons'.

After the intro tune, the face of producer Sally Clark appeared on the screen.

"Good evening," Sally smiled. "This week, *At home with the Altons* is a bit different. I'm sure you have all seen in the papers that Debbie Alton has broken her leg. So she can't do this week's show."

Millions of people sat glued to their TVs.

"So instead," said Sally, "a special group of people are at home with the Altons."

The camera moved round and showed Kate in her room.

"This week," said Kate to the camera, "I thought Mum could see what it's like to live with *my* guests for a change!"

Debbie Alton was watching the TV in her bedroom. What was Kate talking about?

"That's right," grinned Kate. "My Mum is going to see what it's like to live with five teenage girls!"

The camera panned round and showed Jaz and three of Kate's other mates from school – Keira, Jen and Clare.

Kate turned on her stereo and loud music blasted out. The girls started laughing and dancing.

Debbie Alton covered her ears and looked at the TV screen in shock.

"Noooooooo!" she shouted.